Man of ALL SEASONS

STEPHEN DAVIS

Man of
ALL SEASONS
STEPHEN DAVIS

ANGUS
& ROBERTSON
PUBLISHERS

ANGUS & ROBERTSON PUBLISHERS

Unit 4, Eden Park, 31 Waterloo Road,
North Ryde, NSW, Australia 2113;
94 Newton Road, Auckland 1,
New Zealand; and
16 Golden Square, London W1R 4BN,
United Kingdom

First published in Australia
by Angus & Robertson Publishers in 1989

Copyright © Stephen Davis

National Library of Australia
Cataloguing-in-publication data.

Davis, Stephen, 1951-
   Man of all seasons, an Aboriginal perspective of the
   natural environment.
   ISBN 0 207 16180 1.

   1. Seasons — Northern Territory — Arnhem Land. 2.
   Ecology — Northern Territory — Arnhem Land. (3).
   Aborigines, Australian. I. Title.

574.5'43'0994295

Typeset in Melior
Printed in Hong Kong

Malawutjiwuy Wang'kubali
Merriwangalil Gondarra
Mogugu bunhamirri

Oliver, adopted by the
Golumala tribe,
Hunter of Mudskippers

Little black cormorants at Djabiluku billabong

CONTENTS

Yellow clouds of approaching Midawarr.

Preface

ON 17 SEPTEMBER 1932, Aboriginal people from Caledon Bay on the eastern shores of Arnhem Land in the Northern Territory speared five Japanese pearlers and looted their vessel. A sixth Japanese and the vessel's European skipper escaped. The killings were in retaliation for alleged interference with Aboriginal women. Later, two European beachcombers were killed on Woodah Island, approximately 60 kilometres south, for a similar offence.

Constable McColl of the Northern Territory Police was sent from Darwin with an armed party of police and trackers to investigate the killings. He never completed his investigations. On 1 August 1933, he too was speared to death and his party routed by the Aborigines.

In an effort to avert a reprisal by the white population of the Northern Territory, Donald Thomson, an anthropologist from the University of Melbourne, offered his services to the Federal Government under a commission to travel to Arnhem Land and investigate the circumstances that led to the fateful events.

Delayed until 1935, this was the first of three prolonged field trips made by Donald Thomson. During the period from 1935 to 1943 he formed an affinity with local Aboriginal groups and subsequently learnt to speak Gupapuyngu, the lingua franca of the Aboriginal people of northeast Arnhem Land who refer to themselves as Yolngu.

Thomson's training in botany and zoology, together with his knowledge of the bush gained in earlier fieldwork in northern Australia, enabled him to document in detail the Aboriginal seasonal cycle. Much of his voluminous field notes, which are complemented by fine sketches and photographs, remain unpublished and are lodged in the Museum of Victoria.

In the early 1970s my friend Ian Morris rediscovered the intricacies of Aboriginal knowledge of the seasons when he was living at Elcho Island in Arnhem Land. Like Thomson, he was a long-term resident of the area and methodically detailed Aboriginal knowledge of the seasons as he travelled through the bush with the local Yolngu people on weekend and holiday hunting trips.

It was Ian Morris who introduced me to the Aboriginal perspective of the Arnhem Land environment. His commitment to the people and enthusiasm for the bush were infectious. Thus my arrival at Milingimbi, in Arnhem Land early in 1979, was marked

Left *Dawn over the Arnhem Land coast.*

ix

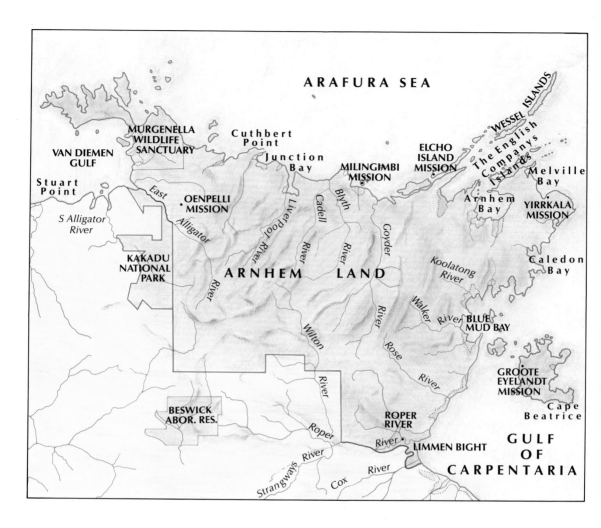

by a flurry of questions that I directed at local Aboriginal people about seasonal activities, and there followed seemingly endless excursions into the bush and along the coast from which I would return at indeterminate times.

This book is not my interpretation of the environment as used by Aboriginal people. Rather, it is the Aboriginal perspective of the natural environment in northern Australia as seen and lived by the Yolngu Aboriginal people, and it has been translated from the Gupapuyngu language.

Aboriginal groups throughout the tropical north of Australia have the same seasonal cycle as the Yolngu Aboriginal group of northeast Arnhem Land. Similarly, Aboriginal groups in other parts of Australia have a seasonal cycle based on local seasonal indicators such as changes in wind direction, animal behaviour, plant flowering and fruiting.

Such an intricate knowledge of the natural environment was once enjoyed by many cultures throughout the world but now, unfortunately, that knowledge is lost forever.

Notes on the text

EVERY PLANT and animal has a scientific name which is written in Latin and, by convention, written in italics. However, many plants, and some animals, do not have a common name. Hence the decision was made to include the scientific name so that the reader may follow up information in other texts using a correct identification, while also using the common English name where it exists.

For each plant and animal mentioned in this book there is of course an Aboriginal name in the Gupapuyngu language. We have considered these Aboriginal names to be a little difficult for the average reader to pronounce and have thus excluded them. However, the Aboriginal name along with the scientific name and common English name are included within a complete Aboriginal taxonomy of the plant and animal kingdoms for the Gupapuyngu language in an earlier publication, *Gupapuyngu Dictionary by Domains: Natural Species*, by this author and published by the Northern Territory University Planning Authority in 1986.

Acknowledgements

Many Aboriginal people have patiently assisted me to acquire Aboriginal knowledge of fauna and flora during daily hunting trips throughout the seasonal cycle over many years. In particular I wish to mention Danyala (Liyagawumirr clan), Munymuny (Ngaymil), Rrikili (Liyagawumirr), Mawalkwuy (Gupapuyngu), Matjarra (Liyagawumirr), Mendjil (Golumala), Yithirri (Gupapuyngu), Marragalbiyana (Gemalangga), Bandharrawuy (deceased), Bella (deceased), Bonga (deceased) and Mamakun (Birrkili). Acknowledgement is also due to Ian Morris whose photographs appear on pages xii, xiii, 5, 9, 28 and 29.

My gratitude is especially due to Julie who was ever-present whether to jury-rig a sail when an outboard motor failed, teach a young magpie goose to fly or critically review the manuscript and photograph selection. She is in every sense a co-author of this book and a Woman of all Seasons.

Over *The grass and undergrowth are cleared away by fire.*

Introduction

THE ANTHROPOLOGIST *Donald Thomson wrote in the following terms of the Yolngu Aboriginal group:*

The natives are familiar with the various botanical (ecological) associations which characterise this territory, and distinguish these by special terms. They can name, without hesitation, the characteristic trees, shrubs and herbaceous plants in every association, as well as food plants and animals, and the raw materials used in technology, which at any season of the year they obtain from each of these associations...

The estuarine reaches, tidal arms, and floodplains yield very large quantities of food—chief of which are fish, for the capture of which many very specialised methods have been developed in Arnhem Land. Shellfish (Maipal), including *latjin* (the wood-boring ship worm, *Teredo*), are also obtained in quantity in the mangrove zone. The shellfish are gathered at low water and Teredo are extracted from sodden logs uncovered at low tide, by splitting these with an axe and pulling them out by hand...

They secure fish, freshwater tortoises and snakes, by swimming "drives" and by use of dams, weirs, traps, nets and special poisons ... (Thomson, D.F., *Economic Structure and the Ceremonial Exchange Cycle in Arnhem Land*, Macmillan, Melbourne, 1949).

Today among Yolngu there is a very close correlation between the changing emphasis on different kinds of marine foods and the movement of Yolngu through the offshore and coastal regions of Arnhem Land during the yearly cycle.

Aboriginal people throughout the tropical north of Australia have a highly detailed knowledge of the movement of various faunal species throughout the biosphere. Especially in regard to marine fauna, Western science has little knowledge as yet of such behaviour. The interplay between fauna and flora is a relationship which lies at the very heart of Aboriginal knowledge and use of the environment. Non-Aboriginal people have largely ignored such relationships because of a preoccupation with detail of individual species.

Similarly, the 'fat' cycle is a phenomenon about which Western biologists know little. The condition of food sources correlates very closely with the seasonal movement of Yolngu populations. this fat-possessing quality, called *djukurrmirri* in the Gupapuyngu language, extends to fish, crustaceans, molluscs, birds, mammals and reptiles.

Left   *Sunset over the Arnhem Land escarpment.*

1

Right *Fast flowing waters of the wet season.*

The seasonal movement pattern varies from a sedentary wet season existence to the highly mobile hunting groups of the dry season and is underpinned with considerations of potential product value and prestige in visiting certain camp sites and particular sites of economic importance. These are often inaccessible at some times of the year or lie a considerable distance from areas of more constant occupation and necessitate some risk, such as in a long voyage, to reach them. Consideration of rights of access to estates punctuate such planned hunting expeditions, while asserting rights of succession to estates may often be the motive for dry-season occupation of sites on mother's and mother's mother's clan estates.

The seasonal Yolngu population movement pattern is thus the product of an interplay between the political, social and economic spheres of Yolngu life as seen by the author during the conduct of daily hunting activities, ritual life and the annual cycle of movement across the land and seascape.

Aboriginal people in northeast Arnhem Land generally recognise six major seasons in the yearly cycle of natural events. Each season is heralded by distinct changes in faunal, floral and climatic conditions. The Aboriginal people view the natural environ as a total, integrated system of which they are a part.

THE ABORIGINAL SEASONAL CALENDAR

The main seasons roughly correspond with our seasonal calendar:

Dhuludur': the pre-wet season in October−November

Bärra'mirri: the growth season in December−January

Mayaltha: the flowering season in February−March

Midawarr: the fruiting season in March−April, including

Ngathangamakulingamirri, the two-week harvest season in April

Dharratharramirri: the early dry season in May−July, including **Burrugumirri,** the time of the birth of sharks and stingrays—three weeks in July−August

Rarrandharr: the main dry season in August−October

Dhulu<u>d</u>ur'
(The Pre-Wet Season)

*THE FIRES are only small and isolated now. The winds
are mixed up, each blowing at different times, often
within the same day. The male thunder shrinks the
waterholes and the female thunder brings the rain.*

THE FIRES are only small and isolated now. They are not
really for hunting. Occasionally there is a big grass fire on
the mainland, but it doesn't last for very long, unlike the fires of
the early dry season and the main dry season that sometimes
burn for days. The tides are big and the floodplains are covered
with water for the first time since the fruiting season in the last
wet. The mosquitoes breed in the pools of water left on the
floodplains as the tide recedes. The sea is flat and the water is
clear. The weather is still cool during the night, like it was in the
main dry season, with mists settling in the stillness of the night
and rising early in the morning after a light northwest wind has
been blowing during the day. The scent of the flowering weeping
paperbark *Melaleuca leucadendron* is sickly sweet as it hangs
heavy in the still air of the late afternoon and evening. Just before
dawn it is cold and the stars shine brightly through clear skies.
The winds are mixed up, the southwest wind, the southeast
wind, the northeast wind and the northwest wind each blowing
at different times, often during the same day.

The white-breasted woodswallows *Artamus leucorhynchus*
arrive, but are only few in number. Magpie-larks *Grallina
cyanoleuca* are still to be found in large numbers. These two
species of birds are only found together for very short periods at
the approach of the wet season and the dry season. The arrival of
the swallows signals the oncoming rain.

Other small birds such as the singing bushlark *Mirafra javanica*,
yellow white-eye *Zosterops lutea* and golden-headed cisticola
Cisticola exilis, come, but do not start to build their nests until

Left   *A storm of the approaching wet season.*

5

Above *The heavy flowering of the weeping paperbark.*

after the rain has brought a lot of growth to the grassland. The singing bushlark sings at night as well as in the day. It eats seed from the ground and runs around under cover of the growing grass. This bird only comes with the rain. After a wet season storm, when everything is quiet, the singing bushlark is the first sound you hear, especially at night.

The 'male' thunder that comes early in the pre-wet season shrinks the waterholes. This thunder is far off and rumbles distantly in the afternoons. The weather begins to get hot and humid as the clouds build up more and more each day. When the sky is covered by heavy cloud most of the day, the 'female' thunder brings the rain. The southwest wind is often the wind which brings this first short rain to start plants growing.

Now that the first rain has come, other winds bring heavy rain. In the afternoon it is warm while the cloud is building up. Then, late in the afternoon, the southeast wind brings blasts of strong, gusty wind. When there are just a few minutes left before the rain hits, the wind becomes very cold. Then the cold rain falls. Although the rain is very heavy, there are no puddles remaining afterwards to show what has happened. The dry earth soaks up all the rain and everything is still.

The green tree frog *Litoria caerulea* starts a chorus of croaking as soon as the rain falls. Soon, the first yellow shoots of grass crack the earth. Within a few hours the shoots are green and momentarily carry the crust of earth up. Each morning there are a few centimetres of new yellow growth on the grass.

Early in the pre-wet season the build-up of storm clouds each week brings rain, followed by a short period of clear weather and northwest winds.

The singing bushlark sings a song to tell that this is the time when things should grow. Everything is clean and fresh because the rain is cold and heavy. This is a very important time because this is like the birth of the whole world. The seasonal cycle is starting again.

Right *The male thunder shrinks the waterholes.*

The pre-wet season is the time when the bush starts to recover noticeably after the fires of the dry season. The first rains bring new shoots of growth all over the bush. The grass shoots appear as a green carpet across the floodplains and savanna grasslands, while the first vines reappear and young eucalypt trees shoot from the floor of the eucalypt forests. The first tendrils on the bush grape *Ampelocissus acetosa* wind their way around the zamia palm *Cycas armstrongii* which displays full fronds of growth; they have recovered from the dry season fires earlier than most plants.

With water still scarce early in the pre-wet season, the swelling in the cajuput tree *Melaleuca cajuputi* is tapped for fresh drinking water. Along the shoreline, the incoming tide brings floating flowers of the pornupan mangrove *Sonneratia alba*. The green plum *Buchanania obovata* is one of the few other plants in flower early in the season. Later, when the first storms come, wild passionfruit *Passiflora foetida*, green plum, geebung *Persoonia falcata* and red apple *Syzygium suborbiculare* bear fruit. These four plants all grow in the eucalyptus forest. Other plants which fruit in the bush during the pre-wet season are grass-leaved convolvulus *Ipomoea graminea*, poison pea *Galactia tenuiflora*, bush potato *Eriosema chinense*, bush gardenia *Gardenia megasperma* and yellow-faced bean *Vigna lanceolata*. Two other plants, native grape *Cayratia trifolia* and the zamia palm, only fruit in the eucalyptus forest in the pre-wet season, although they often fruit in other habitats during other seasons. The long yam *Dioscorea transversa* may still be found. In the monsoon forest the round yam *D. bulbifera* is ready to be dug up and eaten. The finger bean *Vigna radiata* shoots new growth among the dry

Above left *The rains bring a chorus of green tree frogs.*

Above *The first rains come on blasts of cool air.*

leaves which have dropped in the monsoon forest during the dry season. The fires that burnt through the open woodland only singed the edges of the monsoon forest so plants quickly grow with a little rain.

The giant waterlily *Nymphaea gigantea* and the spike rush *Eleocharis dulcis* can be collected only in the large billabongs and waterholes that have retained some water throughout the dry season. With the fresh rain both these plants, as well as bush currant *Vitex glabrata*, shoot new growth in the waterholes, indicating a reliable food source.

As the waterholes shrink early in the season, magpie geese *Anseranas semipalmata* flock to the little remaining water. The high concentration of geese provides an easy target for the Aboriginal hunters concealed in the reeds surrounding the waterholes. Rainbow bee-eaters *Merops ornatus* and varied lorikeets *Psitteuteles versicolor* arrive early in the season. They are joined by azure kingfishers *Ceyx azureus* and a few blue-winged kookaburras *Dacelo leachii* after the first rains.

When the waterholes slowly fill, the wandering whistling-duck *Dendrocygna arcuata*, Pacific black duck *Anas superciliosa* and radjah shelduck *Tadorna radjah* all come to build their nests to breed, so they are fat.

Brolgas *Grus rubicunda* and jabirus *Xenorhynchus asiaticus* get ready to nest. Brolgas dance together when the rain starts.

Above   *Charcoal grill magpie geese.*

Right   *Magpie geese flock to remaining waterholes.*

As soon as plants shoot and the floodplains are covered with new growth, agile wallabies *Macropus agilis* give birth. They wait for the rain so that there will be plenty of food for the young wallabies to grow on. Antilopine kangaroos *Macropus antilopinus* also wait until the rains start on the mainland before they give birth.

Northern brushtail possums *Trichosurus vulpecula* and echidnas *Tachyglossus aculeatus* are fat during the pre-wet season. The northern brown bandicoot *Isoodon macrourus* and the emu *Dromaius novaehollandiae* are still hunted on the mainland.

During this season many lizards are fat and are a good source of food. The northern blue-tongue lizard *Tiliqua scincoides intermedia* is fat because it is ready to give birth to its young. The frilled lizard *Chlamydosaurus kingii* is fat as it has been feeding on all the ground insects that come to live on the new growth brought by the rain. The marbled velvet gecko *Oedura marmorata* is big and fat and it has bright yellow stripes and a thick tail.

Goannas that are also fat are the spotted tree goanna *Varanus timorensis*, the mangrove monitor *V. indicus* and Mertens' water monitor *V. mertensi*.

During the pre-wet season some snakes are thought of not just as snakes, but more as edible meat along with birds, mammals, tortoises, lizards, flying foxes and crocodiles. The olive python *Liasis olivaceus*, the water python *L. fuscus* and the Javan file snake *Acrochordus javanicus* are a few of the snakes which are fat at this time. Burton's legless lizard *Lialis burtonis* is fat also, but it is not sought for food.

Very few bees are seen in the pre-wet season. There is very little honey in the hives so they are only sought when beeswax is required to make artifacts for a ceremony.

As the first rains open up the mud of the dried-up waterholes, the northern long-necked turtle *Chelodina rugosa* and the turtle *Emydura victoriae*, both called tortoises locally, emerge and are prized for their fat condition. Young tortoises are found in the waterholes as the early rains replenish the fresh water. The fat adult tortoises are caught and kept alive until they are eaten, at which time they are cooked in their shells.

The green turtle *Chelonia mydas*, flatback turtle *C. depressa* and hawksbill turtle *Eretmochelys imbricata* are still the most commonly hunted turtles. Before the storms of the wet season the calm seas allow extensive trips to the furthest turtle-hunting grounds.

With the extreme high and low tides of the pre-wet season, false trumpet shells *Syrinx aruanus* and yellow bailer shells *Melo amphora* are found in abundance on the exposed sandbars, especially those surrounding reefs. Co-operative hunting trips of men from various clans are arranged to exploit these shellfish. On the reefs themselves and the rocky shorelines of the outer islands, black-lipped oysters are 'fat' and are constantly harvested by women throughout the pre-wet season.

Above *Oysters growing on mangrove roots.*

Left *Echidnas are fat in the pre-wet season.*

Above *Small-stilted mangroves.*

Below *A delicious hermit crab occupies a lined nerite shell.*

During the late dry season and pre-wet season, daily hunting activities extend to the most seaward regions of Aboriginal marine estates. The calmness of the sea makes travel as safe as possible. The clear sky assists Aboriginal sea voyages which rely in part upon celestial navigation, especially for longer voyages. Such longer voyages and hunting trips extend over many days, often requiring access to several estates and hence requiring representatives of a number of clans in the hunting party.

Close into shore *Paphia hiantina* and *Pinctada maxima* are the main shellfish collected. At the edge of the mangroves, oysters *Saccostrea scyphophilla* are found attached to the aerial roots of the small-stilted mangrove *Rhizophora stylosa*, although this shellfish can be found in abundance on the mangrove roots overhanging the water of small tidal creeks. The lined nerite *Nerita lineata* is yet another shellfish that is found on trees. It does not attach itself to the roots like the oyster does. Rather, it crawls on the roots and the trunk of the tree. Hermit crabs often use lined nerite shells to protect their soft bodies which are delicious when lightly roasted. Oysters are always cooked in hot ashes whereas the lined nerites may be either cooked in hot

ashes or boiled. The shellfish *Polymesoda coaxans* is collected from the mud further into the mangroves. Sometimes the broken shells are found strewn around the mud. They have been crushed by mud crabs *Scylla serrata* which come with the rising tide to look for food. During the pre-wet, mud crabs are no longer fat.

The barramundi *Lates calcarifer* move back to the mouth of the creeks and around the mangroves before they swim up the creeks to breed during the heavy rains. There are so many fish that it is easy to spear them. The threadfin divide into two groups. Sheridan's threadfin *Polydactylus sheridani* move to the creek mouths with the barramundi, while giant threadfin *Eleutheronema tetradactylum* swim out to join other fish around the reefs. Skinnyfish *Scomberoides commersonianus*, spotted trevally *Caranx melampygus* and turrum *Carangoides emburyi* all move out into the deeper water around the reefs. Birds flock to dive at the young white trevally *Caranx nobilis*, which live in the shallow waters surrounding the reefs. It is here that the threadfin swim in the pre-wet season. Barracuda *Agrioposphyraena barracuda* have moved out past the reefs into the deeper water and will return later in the wet season.

Towards the end of the pre-wet season the rain is being brought only by the northwest wind. It rains almost every evening. This is the start of the next season which is signified by heavy rain and growth.

Above A bark painting of mud crabs which have very little meat in the pre-wet season.

Below Calm seas of the pre-wet season.

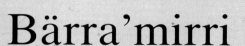

Bärra'mirri
(The Season of Heavy Rain and Growth)

HEAVY RAIN comes every day and the plants grow quickly. Soon there is lush growth throughout the whole bush.

EVERYWHERE PLANTS are growing. The air is warm and the rain makes the earth soft for the young shoots to push their way through to grow.

The heavy rain is brought by the northwest wind. It comes every day, indicating that the pre-wet season is finished and the new season of heavy rain and growth has started. There is no thunder, just heavy rain and strong winds.

The plants grow quickly and soon there is lush growth throughout the whole bush.

In the bush, the stringybark *Eucalyptus tetradonta*, long-fruited bloodwood *E. polycarpa*, cocky apple *Planchonia careya*, and red-flowering kurrajong *Brachychiton paradoxus* trees all have new leaves.

The yams are bright green with their new growth as they climb up the trees. Some yams, such as the long yam *Dioscorea transversa*, are flowering. The yellow-faced bean *Vigna lanceolata*, like the long yam, is also flowering. However, the bean will not be ready to be eaten until the dry season, and although the root of the yellow-faced bean is still growing it can now be eaten.

The fruit of the white berry bush *Securinega melanthesoides*, the red apple *Syzygium suborbiculare* and termite tree *Ganophyllum falcatum*, all of which flowered in the pre-wet season, are now ready to be eaten.

The only other plant food available in any quantity during the heavy rain is the cocky apple and the bush currant *Vitex glabrata*, which are both fruits.

With the growth of hoarehound *Hyptis suaveolens* and grasses such as bunch spear grass *Heteropogon contortus*, an abundance

Left *Heavy rain replenishes the paperbark swamp.*

15

Above   Ripe red apples.

Below   Ducks nest in the wet season.

of insect life soon inhabits the grasslands. Shortly, small birds such as the golden-headed cisticola *Cisticola exilis* and singing bushlarks *Mirafra javanica* are building their nests in the long grass and feeding on the seeds. Other birds such as the white-breasted woodswallow *Artamus leucorhynchus*, forest kingfisher *Halcyon macleayii*, rainbow bee-eater *Merops ornatus* and spangled drongo *Dicrurus hottentottus* constantly search the grass for insects to feed on.

Varied lorikeets *Psitteuteles versicolor* swarm in flocks to the flowering eucalypt trees. Only one or two red-winged parrots *Aprosmictus erythropterus* are to be seen. Flocks of eight to ten red-tailed black cockatoos *Calyptorhynchus magnificus* feed on eucalypt nuts.

As the waterholes and billabongs fill up, magpie geese *Anseranas semipalmata* begin to build their nests. Where the water is still shallow, they wait before building their nests and laying their eggs. The Pacific black duck *Anas superciliosa* and other ducks, such as the radjah shelduck *Tadorna radjah* and the wandering whistling-duck *Dendrocygna arcuata* are building their nests and will hatch their young when the waterholes are full and there will be plenty of food. Wandering whistling-ducks fight a lot during early in the season of heavy rain and do not really settle down until nesting.

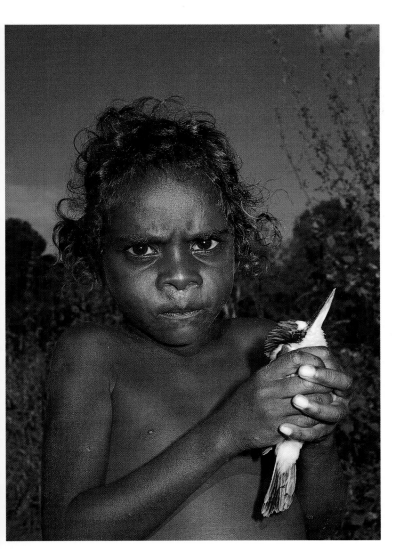

Left An intense hunter captures a forest kingfisher.

Below left Spear grass.

Below A traditional wet season house.

Above *Barramundi are fat in the wet season*

The abundance of water which brings the growth in plants also brings new populations of mosquitoes. Geckos, especially *Hemidactylus frenatus*, gorge themselves on the mosquitoes. In the mangroves there are so many mosquitoes that they deter most hunters. But the mangrove worms are so deliciously fat that even the mosquitoes are tolerated in order to gather them.

To combat the mosquitoes in the swamp areas platforms are often built. The roof is sometimes made of paperbark sheets as was traditionally done but now is more often covered with canvas. A smoking fire is lit on the ground under the platform to deter the mosquitoes.

Mud crabs *Scylla serrata*, which also live in the mangroves, are not fat until early in the dry season. The lined nerite *Nerita lineata* is the only other shellfish which is a significant food source available in the mangroves during the heavy rains.

The black-lipped oyster *Saccostrea echinata* will not be fat again until the northeast wind blows in the dry season. But with the change in weather conditions other shellfish are now fat. These include the turban shell *Turbo cinereus porcatus*, the giant gem chiton *Acanthopleura gemmata*, *Paphia hiantina*, the ark shell *Anadara granosa* and the telescope mud creeper *Telescopium telescopium*.

Along the beaches young tamarind trees *Tamarindus indica* sprout from the seeds that ripened in the dry season. The large tamarind trees are bright green with all their new growth.

Further down on the beach there are sometimes large swarms of dragonflies *Notoneura* sp. They swarm on the northwest wind and hover around the water's edge. Sometimes they hover a little further inland past the beach. When this swarming happens regularly, the sea mullet *Mugil cephalus* and the diamond-scaled mullet *Liza vaigiensis* are fat and can be caught as soon as the seas are calm. Barramundi *Lates calcarifer* can be found swimming lazily along in the quiet water under the over-hanging mangrove trees in the creeks. Soon they will be found in large schools moving around past rocky areas and beaches as they begin to search for food. When barramundi are searching for food like this, they lose the black coloration on their backs that developed when they were laying their eggs near the fresh water. Sheridan's threadfin *Polydactylus sheridani* has left the giant threadfin *Eleutheronema tetradactylum* and is living with the barramundi. They will stay together until later in the dry season. Salmon catfish *Netuma thalassina* and blue catfish *Neoarius australis* are also moving from the creek mouths to the mangroves and are fat. Turrum *Carangoides emburyi* are living around the rocks and small reefs close in to the islands. Skinny-fish *Scomberoides commersonianus* are living with the turrum, but also live along the edge of the beaches when there are very high tides. At this time of year the tides start to become higher than normal. A few days after the full moon the highest tides occur. These are the spring tides. Soon the soil will be soaked with rain and most of the rainwater will lie on top of the soil.

The high spring tides rise up the creeks and meet with the rain water flowing out of the bush. All the water joins together and floods the saltpans and grassy floodplains. These areas stay full of water until the end of the wet season. This is the time when the barramundi swim up across the floodplains and are easily speared in the grass.

Left *Meandering rivers discharge wet season rains.*

The barracuda *Agrioposphyraena barracuda* move back from the deep water and can be caught close to the rocky shore of the islands. They especially like places where the water runs deep and fast. Black-finned long-toms *Tylosurus melanotus* leap up and 'fishtail' across the top of the water, sometimes for long distances. They are good to eat during the heavy rains. Often young long-toms can be seen swimming in the sheltered waters of the creeks, while larger ones are found almost anywhere in the open water.

As the northwest wind brings storms daily, the sea is dirty and rough, so most fishing is done close to shore and around the creeks. Purple tusk-fish *Choerodon cephalotes* and other reef fish are fat but it is often too dangerous to travel out to reefs and other islands because of the weather conditions. There are still plenty of stingrays, but the water is usually too dirty or too rough to be able to see them before they are frightened and swim away.

Sharks such as the black-tipped shark *Carcharhinus melanopterus* and the graceful shark *C. amblyrhynchoides*, which were born in the middle of the dry season, are now living around the mouths of the creeks and along the edges of the mangroves. Later in the wet, they will move further out into deep water and the black-tipped shark will stay around the reefs.

Above   Wet season flood plains.

Opposite   A dugout canoe used to cross wet season waterways.

21

Right Frilled lizards are
fat in the wet season.

Below Flowering
bloodwood heralds the
onset of the flowering
season.

Sometimes there may be a calm day when turtles can be seen, but mostly it is too rough to hunt them. There are no turtle eggs to be collected until the dry season.

The northern long-necked tortoise *Chelodina rugosa* and the tortoise *Emydura victoriae* are coming out of the mud as the rain fills the waterholes, but it is generally too wet to get to the billabongs and waterholes to collect them.

The inundation is so extensive that much of the inland is now one continuous sheet of water joining the billabongs and swamps, which has to be traversed in dugout canoes or bark canoes.

Although a few trees are flowering, there are no bees. Honey is hard to find because there are no bees to track. If a beehive is found, then it will not be fat, so honey is left until the dry season.

The agile wallaby *Macropus agilis* is easy to catch in the swamps, while the antilopine kangaroo *M. antilopinus* is fat and having its young.

Javan file snakes *Acrochordus javanicus* are still fat, as are

22

most other snakes. Black whip snakes *Demansia atra* are common now and will often be seen until the dry season comes. Small snakes, like the moon snake *Furina* sp. and the blind snake *Ramphotyphlops unguirostris*, are common under the leaf litter in the bush.

Goannas are still fat, but they are not often hunted during the heavy rains. Only the northern blue-tongue lizard *Tiliqua scincoides intermedia* and the frilled lizard *Chlamydosaurus kingii* are eaten. They are usually caught only because they live around where Aboriginal people camp. The northern blue-tongue lizard has borne its young and the frilled lizard has become fat on the crickets and other ground insects that come with the wet season.

Soon the wild passionfruit *Passiflora foetida* flowers. Many other plants flower, and the rain becomes infrequent and sometimes stops for several weeks. There are indications that the season of heavy rain and growth is drawing to a close and the season of flowering plants is starting.

Mayaltha
(The Flowering Season)

THE FLOWERING season is a season of very little bush food. It is marked by bright sunny days, occasional rain and an abundance of flowering plants.

THE FLOWERING season is a season of very little bush food. It is marked by an abundance of plants that flower, bright sunny days, cool breezes and occasional rain.

During the early part of the wet season strong winds often brought the rain. The wind then stopped as the rain fell. Now the winds blow hard even when it is raining. The rains do not come daily any more, but only every week or two, heralded by the almost deafening croaking of frogs.

This is the first time flies can be seen. There are many varieties of insects appearing. Butterflies still stay in sheltered areas and are not seen on the grasslands for several weeks. Small insects are abundant in the grassland areas. Juvenile grasshoppers, which cannot fly, crawl all over the grasses.

During the pre-wet season only one type of mosquito was seen. This was the large black one which sucks a lot of blood. It was seen every day. Now the mosquitoes only stay around in large numbers for a couple of days after the rains. The sandflies appear when the sandy soil dries out and they stay until the next rain.

In the freshwater pools left by the rain, the water-boatmen *Corixidae* swim about with tadpoles of all species. The water is full of mosquito larvae.

This change of season brings the time for plants to flower. During the flowering season the trunks of many trees are covered by lush green vines. These vines are generally yams that started their growth with the first storms of the pre-wet season, but will not be fully grown until late in the fruiting season, which is the end of the wet season. The roots of plants such as the yam *Dioscorea sativa* var. *elongata*, the yellow-faced bean *Vigna lanceolata*, grass-leaved convolvulus *Ipomoea graminea* and tar vine *Boerhavia diffusa* can be eaten now although still small.

Left *Waterlilies are edible in the flowering season.*

Other food plants which will not be ready until the fruiting season are the native grape *Cayratia trifolia*, the round yam *Dioscorea bulbifera* var. *rotunda*, the long yam *D. transversa* and the zamia palm *Cycas armstrongii*. They are still only small and will not be fully grown until early in the dry season.

Several other plants are also flowering now, but will not be ready to eat until the early part of the dry season. They include the waxflower *Eriosema chinense*, grass potato *Curcilago ensifolia*, paper berry *Grewia retusifolia*, and yellow hibiscus *Hibiscus tiliaceus*.

The flowering season is a season of very little bush food. The pink lily *Amorphophallus* sp., giant waterlily *Nymphaea gigantea*, blue waterlily *N. capensis*, native rosella *Abelmoschus moschatus* ssp. var. *tuberosus*, bush potato *Microstemma tuberosum* and mangrove fern *Acrostichum speciosum* are some of the plant foods available. Plants which specifically produce a fruit crop in the flowering season include termite tree *Ganophyllum falcatum*, cluster fig *Ficus racemosa*, aspirin tree *Morinda citrifolia*, yellow-flowered jungle tree *Polyalthia* sp., red apple *Syzygium*

26

suborbiculare, wild passionfruit *Passiflora foetida* and white berry bush *Securinega melanthesoides*.

The fruit on the large corypha palm *Corypha elata* are growing bigger and turning brown after flowering in the dry season. When the sand palm *Livistona humilis* flowers, the centre of its trunk is sweet and edible. Sometimes these plants are confused with young corypha palms but they are different.

Among the grasslands and throughout the bush, small plants flower wherever growth is possible. Generally these small plants are like grasses and are only significant in that they confirm that the present season is the flowering season. Most of them are grouped together in a class called *mulmu* in the Gupapuyngu language, which includes grasses, herbaceous plants and most small plants that do not have a woody stem. Some common examples of this group are the herb *Borreria breviflora*, bush everlasting *Gomphrena canescens*, the annual *Heliotropium* sp., the twining vine *Merremia gemella* and the pink flowering vine *Austrodolichos errabundas*. The bush carrot *Cartonema spicatum* looks like any other of these many small flowering plants but unlike the others it will yield a root which can be eaten when

Below *The vivid colours of the flowering season.*

ripe in the dry season. The thick growth of these plants and many grasses provides ideal nesting places for many small birds. By mid season, the golden-headed cisticola *Cisticola exilis* has built its nest and laid its pale blue eggs. The singing bushlark *Mirafra javanica* has built its nest on the ground and can often be heard singing on moonlit nights. During the day when it is nesting it sings to another bushlark which answers while perching in the open grassland.

Often, flocks of white-breasted woodswallows *Artamus leucorhynchus* are joined by several rainbow bee-eaters, or rainbow-birds *Merops ornatus* as they dive close to the grass to catch insects such as grasshoppers. Blue-winged kookaburras *Dacelo leachii* can be seen in small groups early in the morning. In the open eucalypt forest, bar-shouldered doves *Geopelia humeralis* and rainbowbirds can be seen in groups of ten to twelve, sitting in small individual dirt-bowls they have made. They can be approached quite close before flying away and even then only fly to a nearby tree. This is not the usual behaviour of these birds, which are harder to approach at other times of the year. The peaceful doves *G. placida* are found around almost every puddle which the rain has left.

Some young longtail finches *Poephila acuticauda* have already fledged and join the flock.

Red-winged parrots *Aprosmictus erythropterus* arrive in greater numbers, but keep to the higher trees. As the grass, hoarehound *Hyptis suaveolens*, grows higher, the red-winged parrots will come down to perch on it.

Across the mud flats adjacent to the mangroves small snakes, such as the bockadam *Cerberus rhynchops* and Richardson's mangrove snake *Myron richardsonii*, are common.

Below Pink flowering vine of the flowering season.

Midawarr
(The Fruiting Season)

MOST GRASSES are seeding in the season of fruiting plants. The east wind signals the beginning of the time of abundant food. When the mango trees shoot new leaves, which are red, the first southeast wind blows gently in the early morning before sunrise.

THE FRUITING season is the season that the Aboriginal people of northeast Arnhem Land look forward to. There is an abundance of food and the daily storms and strong winds are nearly over.

The northwest wind changes to the northeast, bringing rough seas and heavy waves which crash onto the shore. Early in the season the storms still bring heavy rain daily, often with thunder and lightning. The deep sea is heavy and rolls with big waves. It is considered very dangerous to travel across the sea at this time.

By the middle of the season the wind has changed to the east and the heavy storms are less frequent. Light easterly winds blow throughout most of the day bringing cooler weather.

With the break in the rain, insects quickly set about their work. Ants rebuild nests in the soft soil while wasps collect soft mud for their nests.

When the mango trees shoot new leaves, which are red, the first southeast wind blows gently in the early morning before sunrise. Shortly after sunrise the east wind blows and continues for the rest of the day. The seas are often very flat at this time and it is sometimes hard to see where the sea ends and the sky starts, because the horizon is lost in the reflection of the sky on the sea. This is the time for turtle hunting.

The clouds are still large and vertical, growing higher during the day, just like the storm clouds early in the fruiting season. In the evening, the clouds in the middle and late fruiting season are

Left *Gathering waterlilies.*

Above *Sunrise brings gentle east winds.*

yellow and red, and glow after sunset, while the stars can be seen to shine more brightly in the clear air.

This is the season of fruiting plants. During the early part of the wet season, the bush was thick with plant growth. Many plants flowered during the next season and now those same plants are fruiting. The fruit grows, until finally, a few weeks before the end of the season, most of them are ripe. This is harvest time.

Edible plants are grouped into two categories by Aboriginal people in northeast Arnhem Land. The first category includes plants which bear their crop under the ground. These vegetable or root crops are called *ngatha*. Plants in the second category, called *borum*, usually bear their fruit above ground. There are some exceptions in both categories, such as the zamia palm which bears its fruit above ground but is generally referred to as ngatha.

In the monsoon forest the following plants are the main sources of ngatha in Miḏawarr:

round yam *Dioscorea bulbifera* var. *rotunda*
finger bean *Vigna radiata*
pink lily *Amorphophallus* sp.

The following are the main sources of ngatha or vegetable food available in the open woodland:

long yam *Dioscorea transversa*
cocky apple *Planchonia careya*
grass potato *Curcilago ensifolia*
native grape *Cayratia trifolia*
bush carrot *Cartonema spicatum*
native rosella *Abelmoschus moschatus* ssp. *tuberosus*
flat swamp potato *Microstemma tuberosum*
waxflower *Eriosema chinense*
lily *Typhonium* sp.
zamia palm *Cycas armstrongii*
yellow-faced bean *Vigna lanceolata*
poison pea *Galactia tenuiflora*

The following are the primary vegetable food sources in the fresh waterholes:

fringed lily *Thysanotus tuberosus*
creek lily *Triglochin procera*
giant waterlily *Nymphaea gigantea*
blue waterlily *N. capensis*
mangrove fern *Acrostichum speciosum*

Above *Native rosella.*

Below *Edible waterlilies with paperbarks.*

Right Men painted and dancing in a ceremony.

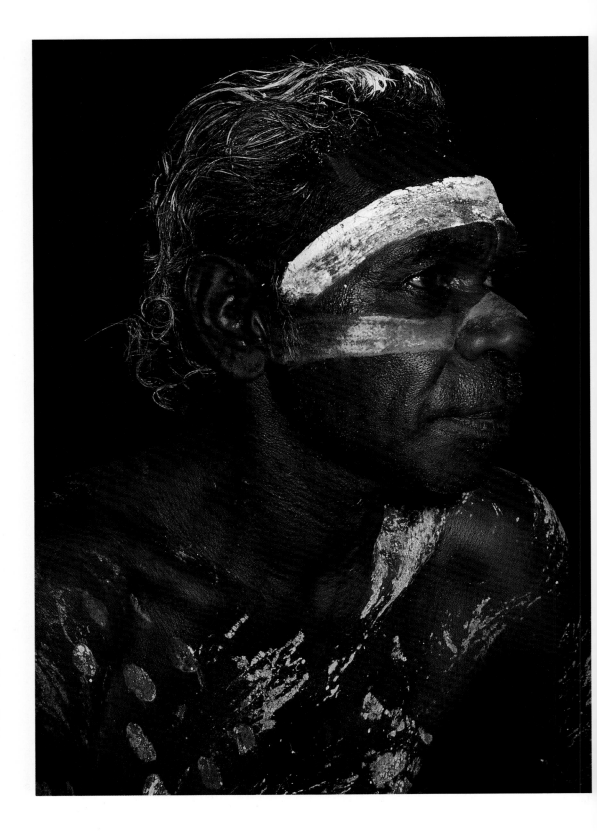

The zamia palm *Cycas armstrongii* is a plant of special significance. Although it fruits throughout most of the year, the majority of the plants bear ripe fruit late in the wet season. At this time the women go off into the bush to collect the nuts. They set up small camps, usually near a fresh waterhole, with paperbark trees close by. After the nuts have been gathered, they are brought back to the camp and stored until there is a large pile. Then the women sit down and husk the nuts by hitting them with a very hard piece of wood. Bags, woven from the bark of the red-flowered kurrajong *Brachychiton paradoxus*, are filled with the small white kernels and placed in a fresh waterhole, being left to soak for three or four days. This process removes the poison from the nuts. The woven string bags are specifically made to allow the water to drain through the bag. These bags are also used to collect the bulbs of the blue waterlily *Nymphaea capensis* and the snowflake lily *Nymphoides indica*. The bulbs are washed in the bag, its open mesh allowing the mud to be washed away.

While the bags of zamia nuts are soaking in the water, the women collect sheets of bark from the nearby paperbark trees *Melaleuca* sp. A bundle of young pandanus leaves *Pandanus spiralis* are also collected and taken to camp. The sheets of paperbark are then fashioned into containers to hold the nuts. The ends of the containers are tied using some of the pandanus leaves which have been stripped and made pliable. The nuts,

Top *The paperbark is fashioned to hold the nuts.*

Above *Zamia palm nuts are ground to a paste.*

Left *Bopi, painted with his clan design.*

Above Prepared and painted for a ceremony.

Opposite above White snowflake lilies.

Opposite below Djurrpun, *the Evening Star, shines at sunset.*

which have started to decompose in the water, are then poured into the bark containers. Handfuls of nuts are squeezed to remove any liquid and then are ground, using a rounded stone. Each woman has her own personal grinding stone. Sometimes these are left at the grinding sites until the next time the nuts are to be ground.

The ground nuts are worked into a very thick paste which is then placed on a piece of paperbark and wrapped up. Strips of pandanus leaf are again used to tie the parcel. A fire is built and when there are sufficient hot ashes, a depression is scraped out in the ashes and the paperbark parcel is buried. It cooks slowly and, when ready, is removed from the ashes and the paperbark peeled back to reveal the food.

This food can be kept for several months, if necessary, but may not be eaten by women and children unless the older men give permission. It is a special food which is prepared by the women for men who are participating in ceremonies at this time of the year. It may also be used by men as part of the payment for a wife. In this case, the man may recruit women of his family group to collect and prepare the food, which he then gives to his future parents-in-law.

Borum, or fruit, is limited to the monsoon forest and the open woodland during the fruiting season late in the wet. In the monsoon forest, fruits which are available include:

fire vine *Malaisia scandens*
wild gooseberry *Physalis minima*
native pomegranate *Capparis umbonata*
Leea rubra
billabong tree *Carallia brachiata*
Drypetes refracta
aspirin tree *Morinda citrifolia*
Allophyllus serratus
sandpaper fig *Ficus opposita var. micracantha*
polynesian arrowroot *Tacca leontopetaloides*
jungle currant *Antidesma ghaesambilla*
tall rod grass *Coelospermum reticulatum*
plum *Santalum album*
broom berry *Randia cochinchensis*

The open woodland provides the following fruit:

wild passionfruit *Passiflora foetida*
paper berry *Grewia retusifolia*
billy-goat plum *Terminalia ferdinandiana*
wild cucumber *Cucumis mela*
bush grape *Ampelocissus acetosa*
Leea rubra
red jungle berry *Drypetes lasiogyna*
aspirin tree *Morinda citrifolia*
tall rod grass *Coelospermum reticulatum*

Above Digging white ochre.

Right Carrying bark to camp to prepare it for painting.

Late in the wet season the blue waterlily *Nymphaea capensis*, giant waterlily *N. gigantea* and white snowflake lily *Nymphoides indica* flower, covering the billabongs with a carpet of colour.

When the waterlily bulbs are being harvested the senior ritual leaders of the Wubulkarra, Walamungu, Gulalay, Batjimurrungu, Guyamirrilil and Wangurri clans make a special ceremony about Djurrpun, the Evening Star (Venus). The Evening Star belongs to all these clans which together make up the Mandjikay ritual group. A string necklace is made from waterlilies and decorated with waterlily bulbs. A messenger wears the necklace to ensure his safe passage through other clan areas as he carries the invitation for the Evening Star ceremony to clans of the Mandjikay group.

When the sap is rising in the stringybark trees the bark is stripped off, heated over a fire and flattened in preparation for bark painting. On the first major hunting excursions of the dry season ochres will be collected for the paintings.

Above Painting on bark with natural ochre and hair brush.

At the same time most grasses are seeding. Sugar grass *Heteropogon triticeus*, bunch spear grass *H. contortus* and river spear grass *Sorghum stipoideum* are over two metres high and starting to bend with the weight of their seeds. Grasshoppers, which were flightless juveniles in the flowering season, now fly up from the grass in large numbers, providing an abundance of food for white-breasted woodswallows *Artamus leucorhynchus* and rainbow bee-eaters *Merops ornatus*. At sunset, the swallows flock to feed on the dragonflies that swarm at the edge of the bush behind the beaches.

Rainbow bee-eaters lay their eggs during the fruiting season in the tunnels they occupy in soft earth mounds. The azure kingfisher *Ceyx azureus* and the forest kingfisher *Halcyon macleayii* fledge their young, as do the blue-winged kookaburra *Dacelo leachii* and the Torresian crow *Corvus orru*. The young forest kingfishers can be seen in groups of four or five, alternately diving at insects while the others perch on branches close by. The young Torresian crows, however, accompany their parents closely, constantly demanding food. Later, in the early dry season, juvenile birds will band together. The barn owl *Tyto alba* and the southern boobook *Ninox novaeseelandiae* juveniles are able to hunt for themselves early in the fruiting season.

The spangled drongo *Dicrurus hottentottus* can frequently be seen singly or in pairs as it flies almost recklessly through the trees in pursuit of insects. The peaceful dove *Geopelia placida* is commonly found in close company with the long-tailed finch *Poephila acuticauda*, the double-barred finch *P. bichenovii*, the chestnut-breasted mannikin *Lonchura castaneothorax* and the pictorella mannikin *L. pectoralis* as they search the ground for seeds.

Further in to the bush the pheasant coucal *Centropus phasianinus* has been busy building a nest throughout the fruiting season. At this time it can be seen breaking small branches from trees and dragging them through the bush to its nest. Frogs and small lizards provide much of its diet. The black-faced cuckoo-shrike *Coracina novaehollandiae* is another common bird of the fruiting season, as are the white-throated honeyeaters *Melithreptus albogularis* and other honeyeaters which are attracted by the many flowering plants. Many will nest and fledge their young late in the fruiting season.

Red-winged parrots *Aprosmictus erythropterus* are common in large numbers among the hoarehound *Hyptis suaveolens*. Other parrots such as the varied lorikeet *Psitteuteles versicolor* and the red-collared lorikeet *Trichoglossus rubritorquis* are captured by the people and the feathers used to make articles for use in initiation, funeral and other ceremonies.

Below *Finches appear in abundance.*

Left   *A young kingfisher.*

Agile wallabies *Macropus agilis* come out of the bush and feed on the grasslands behind the beaches and along the floodplains. The young are generally large enough to feed out of the pouch. No other mammals are regularly hunted during the fruiting season.

Northern blue-tongue lizards *Tiliqua scincoides intermedia*, which were born earlier in the wet season, are now juveniles about 30 centimetres long. Lizards will not be hunted until the dry season.

The northern long-necked tortoise *Chelodina rugosa* and the tortoise *Emydura victoriae* have become fat throughout the early part of the wet season and now lay their eggs, generally above the highest waterline.

Turtles begin to lay their eggs again, but serious hunting for their eggs will not begin until the dry season.

When the new moon rises in the early hours before dawn, some of the older hunters, men and women, wake early and build a fire set apart from the sleeping camp. When the fire is blazing they

Above *Painted with clan symbols for an initiation ceremony.*

Below *Hawksbill turtle.*

take firesticks and throw them at the moon as they sing to ensure a plentiful supply of fish, shellfish, turtles and dugong in the coming dry season.

Young flatback turtles *Chelonia depressa*, which were born last dry season, are now about 45 centimetres in diameter. Turtle hunting is a daily occurrence during the fruiting season, flatback turtles, green turtles *C. mydas*, loggerhead turtles *Caretta caretta* and hawksbill turtles *Eretmochelys imbricata* being common.

Dugong *Dugong dugong* may be hunted at night. They often sleep on the surface and are carried by the sea currents. On moonlit nights they can be found floating in the channels. It is easy to follow the channels because white foam marks the middle of the channel where the dugong sleeps. Hunters quietly follow the white foam line in the moonlight until they see a sleeping dugong and can spear it with harpoons. At other times dugong may be seen in clear water sleeping on the sea floor. They anchor themselves by wedging or digging their tail and flippers into the sea bed.

The dugong is an important totemic animal, so senior men must be consulted when the carcass is butchered. There are many ceremonies connected with the dugong.

The first turtle is generally speared around the time of the last wet season storm. This turtle forms the focus of a turtle hunting ceremony in which all people in the local community participate. The animal is decapitated and the head is given to the captain of

the boat. The internal organs are removed through the neck opening created by the decapitation. A large fire is then built and a layer of stones, each approximately 10 centimetres in diameter, is placed on the firewood. The turtle carcass is then placed on the stones and the fire lit. When the wood has burnt down to coals, the turtle is removed. The hot stones are placed inside the carcass through the neck opening and the carcass is then replaced on the hot coals. When the turtle is cooked, the lower epidermal shell is removed to allow access to the meat. This part of the shell is taken and stood vertically in the sand in an area of the beach immediately adjacent to the fire. A mock turtle hunt then takes place. The women dance in a large circle, surrounding the performance. A man with acknowledged senior ritual status dances as the spearman with harpoon and rope in hand. Several men hold the turtle rope in line as the spearman advances on the turtle shell in the sand, which represents the turtle in the hunt. Each advance and retreat matches another verse in the song cycle that is sung to accompany the dance. This ceremony signals the 'opening' of the turtle hunting season.

The water python *Liasis fuscus* and the king brown snake *Pseudechis australis* are two of the few snakes which are fat during the fruiting season. Both these snakes may be eaten, but both are sacred to some tribes. The black whip snake *Demansia atra* is common in the long grass. They are very fast, but not aggressive unless annoyed. As the storms become less frequent,

Below *Cooking the first turtle of the hunting season.*

47

mangrove snakes withdraw from the mud flats. The smaller
mangrove snakes such as the bockadam *Cerberus rhynchops* and
Richardson's mangrove snake *Myron richardsonii* are not as
frequently seen on the mud flats as they were in the flowering
season. The only one common in the fruiting season is the
white-bellied mangrove snake *Fordonia leucobalia*.

With the growth of so many plants providing food sources in
the bush, there is not as much emphasis on shellfish. Only a
handful of species are eaten during the fruiting season. *Tapes
hiantina* accounts for most of the shellfish collected, while the
balance is made up of *Modiolis proclivis*, *Gafrarium tumidum*,
Pinctada chemnitzi, *P. maxima*, *P. albina*, *Gari togota* and Ward's
volema *Volema cochlidium*. All of these species are fat during
this season. As the next season, the early dry season, approaches,
the black-lipped oyster *Saccostrea echinata* will become fat and
can be found on the rocky shoreline and reefs of outer islands
where the water is clear. The lined nerite *Nerita lineata* will be

collected in great numbers in the mangroves by people hunting for mud crabs *Scylla serrata*.

The heavy rain and high spring tides early in the fruiting season bring flooding along the grass-covered floodplains and the saltpans. The barramundi *Lates calcarifer* may again be found in this shallow water where they are easily speared. Otherwise, barramundi are usually found in the mangroves or around the rocky areas close by.

Sheridan's threadfin *Polydactylus sheridani* live closely with barramundi and skinnyfish *Scomberoides commersonianus*, which have come in from the outer islands and reefs.

Giant threadfin *Eleutheronema tetradactylum*, which were commonly found with skinnyfish early in the wet, have moved out to the shallow offshore reefs to live with great trevally *Caranx sexfasciatus*. Turrum *Carangoides emburyi* move further out from the mainland and join the large barracuda *Agrioposphyraena barracuda* which are returning from deeper water. Towards the

Above *Women glean shellfish.*

Opposite *The victorious hunter with two turrum.*

Below *Early morning mist as the dry season approaches.*

end of the wet, the sea becomes calmer, with the east wind blowing gently. This is the time when purple tusk-fish *Choerodon cephalotes*, pikey bream *Acanthopagrus berda*, black-spot tusk-fish *Choerodon schoenleinii* and most other reef fish are becoming fat.

The changing weather conditions and increased availability of fish and shellfish on offshore islands lead to a general feeling of expectation among Yolngu men, who start to plan hunting expeditions. Older men often sit under tamarind trees on the beaches discussing the weather conditions and the likely abundance of fish and turtle eggs at various offshore locations.

There is considerable prestige attached to the first successful offshore hunting trip of the dry season. The success of the trip must be ensured, for an unsuccessful trip may be an outstanding embarrassment and temporarily diminish a man's power to co-opt people into joint ventures through his accumulated obligations and alliances. Therefore, with mutual understanding of the potential prestige of a successful hunt, senior men discuss possible hunting grounds and the composition of hunting parties which will ensure access to such sites.

Towards the end of the fruiting season, the days are becoming much more like the dry season with early morning mists. But in the small harvest time when most plant food is ready in the bush, the weather often builds up to threaten a storm. Then, when the bunch spear grass *Heteropogon contortus* has dried out and is bending with the weight of seed, one last storm of the wet season comes and flattens it. This storm is brought on the strong southeast wind, which is the main dry season wind. Sometimes isolated fires have already been lit, but the real burning-off is held back until early in the dry season, the next season.

Dharratharramirri
(The Early Dry Season)

THE NIGHTS ARE cool and there is mist early on some mornings. A few weeks after the start of the early dry season large flocks of magpie-larks appear. The southeast wind swings further south to become the south-southeast wind called the trade wind. Fires are lit throughout the bush.

AT THE CONCLUSION of the fruiting season heavy rain comes from the southeast. There may be one storm or several. Before the rain falls the wind blows very hard for a few minutes and the air becomes very cold. This is the harvest time between the fruiting season and the early dry season.

In the early dry season the night sky is again mostly clear of cloud, in contrast to the heavy cloud cover so common in the wet season. The three stars of the constellation called *Djulpan* (the three stars that make up the belt of Orion the Hunter) are clearly seen in the west in the early night sky. The three stars of *Djulpan* are three men, Birrupirru, Djandurrngala and Ngurruwilpil, sitting in their bark canoe as they paddle across the sky. In the early dry season they reach the western horizon before people go to sleep. This is the time when the storms come and knock the grass down.

The strong winds flatten the tall bunch spear grass *Heteropogon contortus*. When the rain has stopped and the southeast wind is blowing constantly and drying out the grass, then the dry season has really started. Even before the grass, hoarehound *Hyptis suaveolens*, starts to dry out, fires are lit throughout the bush. All the grasshoppers and other small invertebrates fly out through the smoke in front of the fires. The white-breasted woodswallows *Artamus leucorhynchus* fill the air as they dive down to catch the insects. The whistling kite *Haliastur sphenurus*

Left *Fires quickly spread through the dry speargrass.*

53

Above Zamia palms
burnt by the fires.

and the black kite *Milvus migrans* and an occasional crested hawk *Aviceda subcristata* soar on the warm air from the fires as they look for small mammals or reptiles escaping from the fire. Occasionally the black kites swoop in among the swallows to catch insects in their claws. Flocks of Torresian crows *Corvus orru* sit in the trees close to the fire to watch and catch any insects they may see. These big flocks are young crows which were born in the flowering season or early in the fruiting season. This is the last time there will be a lot of swallows around until the wet season.

After the first storm in the early dry season the winds vary in direction. Heavy dews come with the light east-southeast to southeast wind that blows every night. The nights are cool with mist early on some mornings. When we are well into the early dry season the southeast wind swings further south and becomes southeast to south-southeast and is stronger. This is when the mango flowers and there is not enough grass left to burn off. Soon after, the new grass starts to grow through the ashes and the fresh shoots or 'green pick' provide good feed for wallabies. Zamia palms *Cycas armstrongii*, which were burnt by the fires, start to grow new fronds. The taller zamia palms, which did not have all their foliage burnt off in the early fires, start to grow new fruit which will be picked early in the main dry season. The saltpans dry out and the small succulent plant *Arthrocnemum leiostachyum* turns red.

Plants which provide food during the early dry season come mainly from the bush and in and around waterholes. The roots of the bush foods edible during the early dry season are:

Right Crested hawks
hunt on the thermals from
the fires.

54

wax flower *Eriosema chinense*
grass-leaved convolvulus *Ipomoea graminea*
yellow-faced bean *Vigna lanceolata*
poison pea *Galactia tenuiflora*
bush gardenia *Gardenia megasperma*
long yam *Dioscorea transversa*

Food from in and around waterholes are:
spike rush *Eleocharis dulcis*
blue waterlily *Nymphaea capensis*
giant waterlily *N. gigantea*
common wedge fern *Lindsaea ensifolia*

Some billy-goat plums *Terminalia ferdinandiana* are still available, although they really belong to the fruiting season which has just finished. It is the only plant which fruits during the early dry season. Soon the wild peach *T. carpentariae* begins to ripen and will bear fruit through to the main dry season.

Many plants are important during the early dry. Some flower and, by so doing, help indicate that it is the dry season. The long-berried shrub *Diospyros maritima* and the milkwood *Alstonia actinophylla* are two such plants.

Other plants flower and are important because they will fruit in a later season. Some of these plants are:

green plum *Buchanania obovata*
red apple *Syzygium suborbiculare*
cocky apple *Planchonia careya*
big green plum *Planchonella pohlmaniana*
bush grape *Ampelocissus acetosa*
wild asparagus *Asparagus recemosus*
geebung *Persoonia falcata*

Above   *Salt pans dry out and crack.*

Right   *Zamia palms shoot new fronds after the burn.*

Above Waterlily bulbs are gathered for food.

Left Wild peach ripens in the dry season.

Top Drying pandanus
leaves for weaving.

Right Weaving.

Early in the dry season women often collect young pandanus leaves which they strip and dye to weave baskets. The dyes are generally made from the roots and bulbs of plants. The root of the aspirin tree *Morinda citrifolia* makes a particularly bright yellow dye and is often sought because of the bonus of its juicy fruit.

A few weeks after the dry season starts, large flocks of magpie-larks *Grallina cyanoleuca* appear. They sometimes lay their eggs in a swallow's old nest during this time.

When the early fires are finished the insects have nearly all gone. Birds, like swallows, sulphur-crested cockatoos *Cacatua galerita*, the azure kingfisher *Ceyx asureus*, the red-winged parrot *Aprosmictus erythropterus*, the blue-winged kookaburra *Dacelo leachii* and the spangled drongo *Dicrurus hottentottus* also begin to leave. The varied lorikeet *Psitteuteles versicolor* and the red-collared lorikeet *Trichoglossus rubritorquis* stay for a few more weeks, feeding on the woollybutt *Eucalyptus miniata*. A few rainbow bee-eaters *Merops ornatus* stay until well into the early dry season, then leave when their young ones have their tail feathers.

Above King brown snakes are caught for food in the early dry season.

Almost all the finches have gone. A few, such as the longtail finch *Poephila acuticauda* and double-barred finch *P. bichenovii*, stay on in reduced numbers, almost until the end of the early dry season.

The black-faced cuckoo-shrike *Coracina novaehollandiae* stays until the middle of the season, long after the yellow white-eye *Zosterops lutea* has fledged its young and gone. The whistling kite *Haliastur sphenurus* and the Torresian crow *Corvus orru* stay right through the early dry season. The willie wagtail *Rhipidura leucophrys* comes early in the season. The peaceful doves *Geopelia placida* and the bar-shouldered doves *G. humeralis* move away from the thick forest to look for seeds and water. This is when a few emerald doves *Chalcophaps indica* are also seen away from the thick forest, but they only look for water, then quickly return.

Occasionally a flock of red-tailed black cockatoos *Calyptorhynchus magnificus* can still be seen. In the first weeks of the season darters *Anhinga melanogaster* hatch their young and near the end of the season the young darters are almost able to fly.

Many snakes are active throughout this season. Four snakes are commonly caught for food. They are the Javan file snake *Acrochordus javanicus*, the water python *Liasis fuscus*, the olive python *L. olivaceus* and the king brown snake *Pseudechis australis*. Other snakes which are common but not eaten are black whip snakes *Demansia atra*, green tree snakes *Dendrelaphis punctulatus*, death adders *Acanthophis antarcticus*, white-bellied mangrove snakes *Fordonia leucobalia*, Stokes sea snakes *Astrotia stokesii* and moon snakes *Furina sp.*

The only lizards which are generally important as food at this time of year are the mangrove monitor *Varanus indicus*, Gould's goanna *V. gouldii*, Mertens' water monitor *V. mertensi*, the marbled velvet gecko *Oedura marmorata* and the northern blue-tongue lizard *Tiliqua scincoides intermedia*.

Top *Crested Terns nesting.*

Above *Northern blue-tongue lizards are fat in the dry season.*

Opposite *Washing Polymesoda coaxans shellfish.*

A variety of honey is found in the open woodland and the mangroves and is used as food.

At night fruit bats are commonly found throughout the bush. Both the little red flying-fox *Pteropus scapulatus* and the black flying-fox *P. alecto* squeal noisily throughout the night. They are an important source of food because of the fat they have at his time of year.

The northern long-necked tortoise *Chelodina rugosa* and the tortoise *Emydura victoriae* are often easy to catch as the water dries up around the billabongs.

The lined nerite *Nerita lineata* and the *Polymesoda coaxans* are the only shellfish which are significant in the mangroves during this season. Not all shellfish which were eaten earlier in the year taste good during the dry season—with changes in the weather conditions the taste of some shellfish changes. Shellfish which are eaten at this time of the year are the faded sunset shell *Asaphis deflorata, Tellina linguafelis, Tapes variegata,* the turban shell *Turbo cinereus porcatus, Gari togata,* the ark shell *Anadara granosa, Septifer bilocularis, Lopha folium, Gafrarium tumidum, Donax cuneata, Modiolis proclivis, Nerita polita* and *N. albicilla.*

Crustaceans which are common in this season include mud crabs *Scylla serrata,* both mature and immature, sand crabs *Portunus pelagicus,* horn-eyed ghost crabs *Ocypode ceratophthalma* and fiddler crabs *Uca* sp.

Preparations are completed for the first of the dry season hunting expeditions to offshore islands and other coastal localities

Above Danyala excavates a turtle's nest.

Below Green turtle coming ashore to nest.

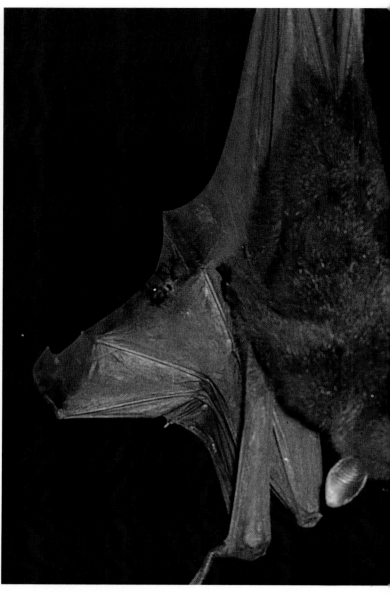

that are still not accessible by land because of flooding. The shafts of turtle harpoons have often been renewed. New ropes have been woven and fitted to the harpoon tips which have been ground to a fine point.

If the northwest monsoons persist into early May, it is very likely that the first major hunting expedition will coincide with the nesting of the crested tern *Sterna bergii*. The crested tern lays a single egg on the sand immediately adjacent to the beach, above the high-water mark. Approximately one week later a second egg may be laid. The eggs are much sought after by Yolngu. Turtle eggs are invariably found very close to the crested tern colonies. There is considerable social pressure to time the

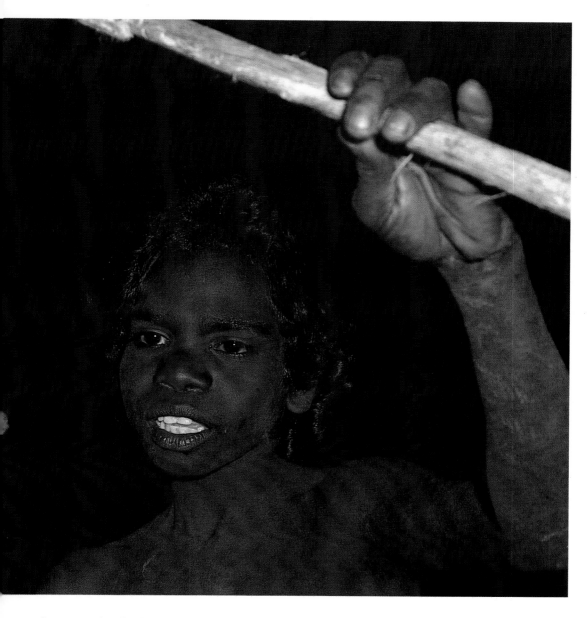

expedition so that both an abundance of turtle eggs and crested tern eggs are collected. To arrive at the tern colony before the first egg is laid or, later, when embryos have formed in the eggs, thus making them unsuitable for consumption, is a considerable embarrassment to the hunters and one which will not quickly be forgotten by other senior men. The lack of success of an expedition caused by any one of a number of circumstances, such as inappropriate timing of the hunt, inexperienced boat handlers or unreliable equipment, may compromise the social and political status of the senior organisers of the hunt.

The sea is the most significant place for food during the early dry season. Barramundi *Lates calcarifer*, Sheridan's threadfin

Above *Flying foxes are caught for food.*

Above *Cleaning a catch of barramundi and skinnyfish.*

Above right *Reef fish are often boiled.*

Opposite *Djoymi eating a turtle hatchling.*

Polydactylus sheridani and the giant threadfin *Eleutheronema tetradactylum* are the most important fish because of the large amount of fat they have. Other fish which are a common food source during this time are: skinnyfish *Scomberoides commersonianus*, salmon catfish *Netuma thalassina*, diamond-scaled mullet *Liza vaigiensis*, pikey bream *Acanthopagrus berda*, mangrove jack *Lutjanus argentimaculatus*, purple tusk-fish *Choerodon cephalotes*, estuary rock cod *Epinephelus tauvina*, and sea mullet *Mugil cephalus*.

Yolngu start fishing in earnest and often set up one-day or overnight hunting camps in the early dry season. On an overnight hunt, the catch on the first day is cooked and the hunters eat their fill. The catch on the second day and the cooked remainder of the first day's catch are returned to the main camp at the end of the hunt. For long trips, only the catch from the final two days is returned to the main camp or settlement. Turtles are kept live for the return journey. The location of turtle nests are noted, excavation often being left until the final days of the hunt so as to minimise cartage and ensure the freshness of the eggs. Occasionally the hunters arrive only to find the eggs already hatching.

Although most of the five common marine turtles can be found at some time in the early dry season, the green turtle *Chelonia mydas* and the flatback turtle *C. depressa* are the most common.

When the southeast wind blows stronger in the latter half of the season most fish that live near the reefs move away to sheltered water near the shore. Skinnyfish can often be found near the barramundi, which come in to feed on the small club mangrove *Aegialitis annulata* around the rocky areas of mangroves. Where the club mangrove grows in the mud, Sheridan's threadfin and giant threadfin come in and use their long whiskers to find food in the muddy water.

When the fruit of the pandanus *Pandanus spiralis*, starts to change from green to red, the early dry season is nearly finished. As soon as the first fruit drops to the ground the flatback turtle starts to lay its eggs. At the same time the red-flowering kurrajong *Brachychiton paradoxus* has lost all its leaves and begins to flower. This indicates that sharks are giving birth to their young and the early dry season is over.

Above   *Small club mangrove.*

Right   *Fern-leafed grevillea are heavy with nectar.*

66

Above *A seasonal hunting camp.*

Far left *Pandanus fruit ripening.*

Left *Red-flowering kurrajong indicates that sharks are being born.*

    The next season, the main dry season, does not start immediately. The northeast, southwest and southeast winds vary for a few weeks and many paperbark swamps dry up completely. These are signs that the early dry season has finished.

    The aspirin tree *Morinda citrifolia* produces fruit and the flowers of the fern-leafed grevillea *Grevillea pteridifolia* produce nectar. Bees produce nectar from the flowers of the broad-leafed carbeen *Eucalyptus confertifolia*. The deep-gold wattle *Acacia torulosa* is also flowering, indicating that sweetlip *Lethrinus chrysostomus* fish are good to eat. The flowering of the pale-barked wattle *Acacia auriculiformis* indicates that turtles have a lot of fat. When the winds settle down the main dry season will start.

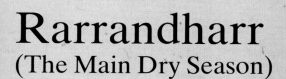

Rarrandharr
(The Main Dry Season)

THE WARM southeast wind blows as the pandanus fruit
begins to fall to the ground. Sharks are giving birth to
their young and are eagerly hunted in the clear shallow
waters that surround the islands. As soon as the
stringybark flowers, snakes lay their eggs and all types
of honey are found in abundance.

THE EARLY dry season is coming to an end when the red-flowering kurrajong *Brachychiton paradoxus* starts to lose its leaves. At the same time the pandanus *Pandanus spiralis* starts to fruit and the east-southeast wind blows. The cold mornings and the mists are nearly gone. Sharks are giving birth to their young. This is an intermediate season between the early dry and the main dry season. It is very short, lasting only a few weeks. Stingrays, such as the brown stingray *Dasyatis fluviorum*, the cowtail ray *D. sephen* and the rat-tailed ray *Gymnura australis*, are fat. The flowering of the green plum *Buchanania obovata* indicates that the stingrays are fat.

During this intermediate season, small sharks and stingrays are cooked in a special way. First the liver is cut out and washed in clean water, then the rest of the body is cooked on hot ashes. The soft backbone, head and tail are removed after cooking. The meat is then kneaded and washed with fresh water. The liver is lightly cooked on the hot ashes for a few moments, cut up and kneaded through the meat. This makes it sweet.

The warmer southeast wind starts to blow and the fruit of the pandanus, which turned red when sharks gave birth, begins to fall to the ground. This indicates that there will soon be lots of turtle eggs on the islands further out to sea and that the turtles themselves will be full of fat. This is the start of the main dry

Left   *Clear waters surround an island in the dry season.*

season; when the turkey bush *Calytrix exstipulata* is in full bloom the season is underway.

During this season all five species of turtles are fat. Each turtle has several different types of fat. Unlaid yellow eggs are fat, green fat is attached to the inside of the shell, yellow fat is sometimes found inside the stomach, and round fat is found near the back legs. The round pieces of meat around the shoulders and the long piece of meat in the shoulders also contain a lot of fat.

Turtles' eggs are usually found high on the beach. The large ones are from the flatback turtle *Chelonia depressa*, which lay up to 50 eggs, while the smaller eggs are from the Pacific ridley *Lepidochelys olivacea*, green turtle *Chelonia mydas* and hawksbill turtle *Eretmochelys imbricata*, which lay around 100 eggs. The eggs of the loggerhead turtle *Caretta caretta* are never found because, Yolngu say, they lay their eggs out on the sandbars in the water.

Above   Danyala with a good catch of young sharks.

Right   Preparing shark meat with liver.

Opposite   Final touches to the body paint for a dhapi (initiation).

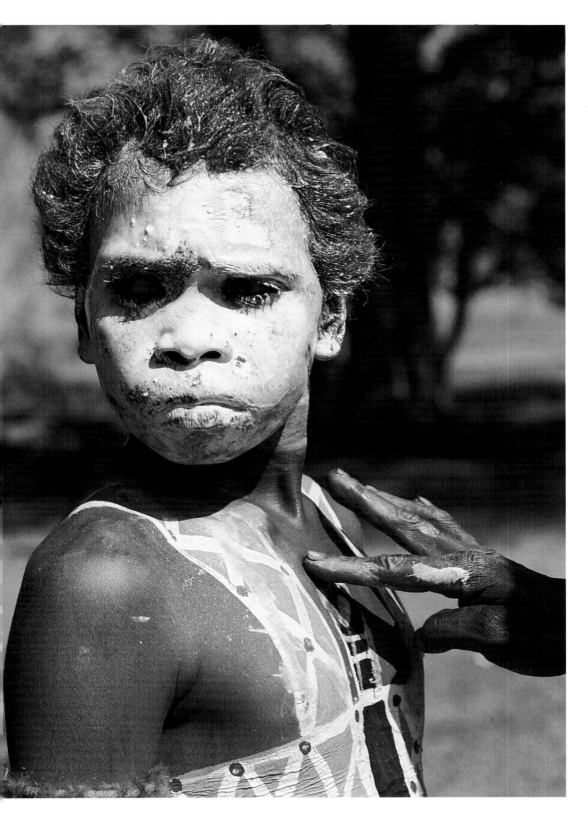

When the wind dies down and the sea is very calm the old hunters know that soon the three stars of *Djulpan* (the belt of Orion the Hunter) will begin to rise in the east after having disappeared on the western horizon early in the dry season. When they see *Djulpan* rising before people go to sleep at night, they know that the goannas will come out during the day, along with other animals, which will be fat at this time of year. It is time then to burn the last of the grass and hunt goannas, wallabies and bandicoots.

Most ceremonies are held in the main dry season when the cold weather is past, there is an abundance of marine food to support the large number of people that come together, and the heavy growth in the bush has been burnt off making travelling easier. Such ceremonies may last from a few days to a week, as in the case of most mortuary rites, or several weeks and months as in the case of those ceremonies which seek to ensure the continuity of life. The culminating performance of very important ceremonies often involves hundreds of people.

Some families use the performance of major ceremonies, for which key Aboriginals are gathered together, as an opportunity to stage an initiation ceremony for their children, marking the transition from childhood to adulthood.

These ceremonies are accompanied by elaborate body painting detailing the totemic association of the novice with the

Above   Mangawila paints his daughter for a Ngarra ceremony.

Opposite   Feathered adornments complete the novice's initiation dress.

75

clan's estate. Senior ritual leaders oversee the preparation and performance of the ceremony and formally initiate the novice's instruction in the law.

On some beaches Gould's goanna *Varanus gouldii* comes down early in the morning and digs up the turtle nest. It eats as much as it can, often returning later to eat any eggs that remain.

The mangrove monitor *V. indicus* is also fat at this time of year and is often hunted when a group of people are hunting for mud crabs *Scylla serrata* in mangroves.

Mud crabs are also hunted in the clear water of the estuaries on the larger islands. In these localities Aboriginal people are mindful of the deadly sting of the stone fish, which is treated with the heated stem and leaves of the goat's foot convolvulus *Ipomoea brasiliensis*.

The northern brown bandicoot *Isoodon macrourus*, antilopine walleroo *Macropus antilopinus*, agile wallaby *M. agilis*, brolga *Grus rubicunda*, magpie goose *Anseranas semipalmata* and emu *Dromaius novaehollandiae* are all hunted during the main dry season. Emus are particularly fat because they lay eggs during this part of the dry season. Magpie geese especially like the root of the spike rush *Eleocharis dulcis* from the billabongs at this time of year, while emus like the fruits of *Verticordia* sp. and the sand palm *Livistona humilis*, which are seeding. The red-flowering kurrajong *Brachychiton paradoxus* soon seeds after the onset of the main dry season, providing one of the sources of edible fruit.

Right *Snakes lay their eggs when the stringybark flowers.*

Other fruits available during the main dry season are:

cocky apple *Planchonia careya*
geebung *Persoonia falcata*
orange spike berry *Mimusops elengi*
wild asparagus *Asparagus racemosus*
red apple *Syzygium suborbiculare*
green plum *Buchanania obovata*
peanut tree *Sterculia quadrifida*
corypha palm *Corypha elata*

Root crops found in the bush during the dry season includes:
fern-leafed grevillea *Grevillea pteridifolia*
round yam *Dioscorea bulbifera* var. *rotunda*
long yam *D. transversa, D. nummularia*
finger bean *Vigna radiata*
grass-leaved convolvulus *Ipomoea graminea*
bush gardenia *Gardenia megasperma*
waxflower *Eriosema chinense*
yellow-faced bean *Vigna lanceolata*
Lindsaea ensifolia

Food found in fresh water includes:

spike rush *Eleocharis dulcis*
blue waterlily *Nymphaea capensis*
giant waterlily *N. gigantea*

As soon as the stringybark *Eucalyptus tetradonta* flowers, all snakes lay eggs and all types of honey are found in abundance. This only happens at the start of the main part of the dry season and is another sign used to tell the season.

Above left Northern brown bandicoot are fat in the dry season.

Above Red-flowering kurrajong seeds are edible.

The trees where bees make their hives are:

coastal paperbark *Melaleuca acacioides*
rough-barked gum *Eucalyptus ferruginea*
stringybark *E. tetradonta*
woollybutt *E. miniata*
long-fruited bloodwood *E. polycarpa*
white mangrove *Avicennia marina* var. *resinifera*
pale-barked wattle *Acacia auriculiformis*

There are four main types of honey and hives. One is made by a very small black bee which builds a large hive in the top of a tree. Another can be found in trees in the mangroves. The third type is made by large vicious bees that build in the tops of trees and the fourth is made in either small ant and termite mounds or tall termite mounds.

When the light breezes are blowing offshore the sea is very flat and the water is clear. The mangrove tree *Sonneratia alba* flowers early in the main dry season, indicating that the diamond-scaled mullet *Liza vaigiensis* are fat and sea mullet *Mugil cephalus* are losing their fat because they are laying their eggs.

Barramundi *Lates calcarifer* are moving down out of the creeks to join the Sheridan's threadfin *Polydactylus sheridani* around the edge of the mangroves. Barramundi have a black back, showing that they still possess the fat from when they were breeding in the fresh water at the head of the creeks. Giant threadfin *Eleutheronema tetradactylum* have moved out to the reefs with the skinnyfish, *Scomberoides commersonianus*, and coral cod *Cephalopholis miniatus* are losing their fat.

Right *Delicious honey is found in abundance in the dry season.*

Above *Giant threadfin move out to the reef in the dry season.*

Left *Mullet are fat when mangroves flower.*

Most fish which have fat during the main dry season live around the reefs. They are:

black-spot tusk-fish *Choerodon schoenleinii*
sweetlip *Lethrinus chrysostomus*
red emperor *Lutjanus sebae*
diamond fish *Monodactylus argenteus*
yellow emperor *Diploprion bifasciatum*
great trevally *Caranx sexfasciatus*

On the outer islands where most reef fish live, the large black oysters, which are found during the main dry season, are fat. Other oysters, such as *Saccostrea scyphophilla* and *Lopha folium*,

are found in similar habitats, providing an ample food source. The lined nerite *Nerita lineata* and *Polymesoda coaxans* are still collected from the mangroves, as is the mangrove worm, which is found in several mangrove trees. Large land snails *Xanthomelon pachystylum* and *X. spheroiderum* are still collected and eaten during the main dry season.

The young saltwater crocodiles *Crocodylus porosus*, which were born late in the wet season, can now be seen sleeping on their mother's back. Other animals that are good sources of food in the dry season are the northern blue-tongue lizard *Tiliqua scincoides intermedia*, frilled lizard *Chlamydosaurus kingii*, Gould's goanna *Varanus gouldii*, mangrove monitor *V. indicus* and northern long-necked tortoise *Chelodina rugosa*. The short-necked tortoise *Emydura victoriae* are fat and can be found in the mud as the fresh waterholes dry out.

When the fire-stick tree *Guettarda speciosa* flowers, the reef fish, such as the black-spot tusk-fish *Choerodon schoenleinii* and purple tusk-fish *C. cephalotes*, are fat. At the same time the bush

lily *Crinum asiaticum* flowers, indicating that snakes such as the king brown snake *Pseudechis australis*, water python *Liaisis fuscus*, olive python *L. olivaceus* and Javan file snake *Acrochordus javanicus* are fat because they are ready to lay their eggs.

Birds which are fat during the main dry season are the magpie goose *Anseranas semipalmata*, brolga *Grus rubicunda*, jabiru *Xenorhynchus asiaticus*, Pacific black duck *Anas superciliosa* and wandering whistling-duck *Dendrocygna arcuata*. Other birds which are commonly seen at this time are the magpie-lark *Grallina cyanoleuca*, Torresian crow *Corvus orru*, blue-winged kookaburra *Dacelo leachii*, pelican *Pelecanus conspicillatus*, sulphur-crested cockatoo *Cacatua galerita* and many finches.

When the mangoes are nearly finished, the dry season is also near its end. The flying foxes, which came to eat the mango fruit in the main dry season, have nearly all gone. When the first white-breasted woodswallows *Artamus leucorhynchus* arrive, the pre-wet season is about to begin. The weather changes and the thunder begins.

Above Saltwater crocodile.

Over Dry season sunset through an orange smoke haze.

81